PORTRAIT
OF MY
FAMILY

Portrait Of My Family

My Family Heritage

FROM GENERATION TO GENERATION

Portrait Of My Family

Edited by F. Michael Carroll

Copyright© September 1978
Carriage House Publications, Ltd.
28 Bridle Road
Redding, Connecticut 06896

ISBN 0-89786-007-1   Library of Congress Card No. 78-61414

My Family Story

Its Past, Present and Future

This Book is Lovingly Dedicated To:

_____

and Recorded By: _____

_____

Date Started: _____

_____

Table of Contents

From Generation to Generation

Genealogy—the tracing of one's ancestors—used to be the special privilege of aristocratic families. Each generation of a wealthy or titled clan employed a historian who kept a careful register of family members past and present. But today we know that nobility does not hold a unique claim on genealogy. Every one of us is the product of a long and fascinating heritage. Moreover, creating and maintaining a family chronicle need not be the task of a professional genealogist. Your ancestry can and should be something you take pride and pleasure in recording.

Why? You have two parents, each of whom had two parents of their own. These four grandparents, in turn, each had a set of parents, too. Within a short span of four generations, therefore, you can count fourteen people from whom you are directly descended. The plot gets thicker and the relations more numerous as you go back in time. Everyone, in other words, bears the genes of countless other individuals, each one with different physical traits and distinct personalities. What you are is the sum of what they were, so that tracing your ancestors becomes a process of self-revelation. Whether the focus is on you alone or on the entire family, the investigation answers fundamental questions about yourself: Who am I? Why am I the kind of person I am, looking the way I do, living where I live, and believing what I believe?

In another sense, completing this register is a way of bringing the past to life by recording people and events from your personal viewpoint rather than from the impersonal, public vantage of history books. Most of us know who fought and won World War I and World War II.

But if you or an ancestor took part in the combat or lived through the wartime period, then those distant episodes become vital segments of your own story.

Producing a record of the present is as important as recounting the past. Remember that history is not merely a narrative of bygone years, but an ongoing event in which you and your family are living participants. And whatever facts or memories you set down here will provide a point of departure for your descendents' genealogies— in which you will be a historical figure. If you don't preserve what you know, later generations will be deprived of crucial information. The passage of time, after all, depletes the storehouse of available data, since the people with whom you grew up may be no more than vague names in the future.

How to Use This Book

The first section is designed to help you make a family tree that fixes your ancestry six generations back to your great-great-great grandparents. Although you may not know all of their names and dates, if you read the chapter on genealogical research at the back of the book, you will discover that with a little effort many of them can actually be traced.

A generation is a step in a person's or a family's lineage that is marked by a birth. When a child reaches adulthood and has children of his or her own, a new generation is created. Family genealogies usually assign numbers to each generation. With respect to your ancestors you may be, for example, the tenth generation in your family line. However, since you are the author of this history, consider yourself the first generation and count backwards, your parents being the second, your grandparents the third, and so on.

Every entry in the genealogical charts is followed by a number that provides a generational code for each particular person in the family. Although it is not essential, you can use these "key numbers" as a shorthand code. Thus, if the husband's father is 3 and you want to identify his brothers, sisters or their children in the section titled "The Family of the Husband's Father," or "Family Gatherings," you enter the key number 3 followed by the relationship "brother *or* sister—niece *or* nephew" and then the name. This system works for all other sections of the book as well.

In the pages following the family tree you can write a longer, more descriptive account of the people in each generation. This section comprises first the husband's relations and then the wife's. Begin by filling in the vital statistics of the people involved—their names, when and where they were born, and the date and place of their deaths. Because some members of a family, through death or divorce, may have been married more than once, there is also space for the names of the spouses and children of these unions. If your present family is the product of a remarriage, you can thus record those people who form part of your history, but to whom you are not related by blood or in a direct line of descent. Use the remaining space to expand the bare statistics. The ancestors section is followed by twenty-five additional categories that will enable you to develop a more detailed and comprehensive history. You can limit each category in your own way, describing just yourself or including other members of the family as well. When you have completed the book, you will have written a unique story, a story unlike any other. This story is the precious record of your heritage.

My Genealogy

My Full Name _____

Birth Date _____

Birth Place _____

Father's Full Name _____

Mother's Full Name _____

Brothers and Sisters _____

My Parent's Courtship

When They Met _____

Where They Met _____

Their First Date _____

Their First Gifts _____

The Proposal _____

The Engagement Party _____

My Parent's Marriage

This Certifies that _____
and _____
Were United in Holy Matrimony _____
Place of Ceremony _____
City _____ **State** _____
Month _____ **Day** _____ **Year** _____
Married by _____

Father's Family

Full Name _____

Birth Date _____

Birth Place _____

Full Name of Father _____

Full Name of Mother _____

Brothers and Sisters _____

Mother's Family

Maiden Name _____

Birth Date _____

Birth Place _____

Full Name of Father _____

Full Name of Mother _____

Brothers and Sisters _____

My Foreign-Born Ancestors

Most families can trace their history back to another country, so list below any ancestors that emigrated from a foreign land. In some cases, your ancestral roots may spread throughout several countries, giving you a rich and diverse heritage. Where did these ancestors come from, when did they arrive, and where did they land? How did the present branch of the family come to settle where it did? And because not all members of a family necessarily emigrate from their homeland, record the names of those who still live in your family's country of origin and how they are related to the people who did emigrate.

The Lands Of My Ancestors

The country or countries where your ancestors came from probably had a different kind of government and different customs from the one in which you now live—and possibly a different language as well. All of these things helped to form the character of your present family, its mode of life, and may even have determined the trade or profession some members took up in the new country. Write down here what you know or have learned about the foreign places where your ancestors were born.

My Family Tree

Father's Ancestry

FATHER'S FULL NAME - 2

DATE OF BIRTH

PLACE OF BIRTH

DATE OF MARRIAGE

PLACE OF MARRIAGE

DATE OF DEATH

PLACE OF BURIAL

OCCUPATION

SPECIAL INTERESTS

MY FULL NAME - 1

DATE OF BIRTH

PLACE OF BIRTH

OCCUPATION

BROTHERS AND SISTERS

GRANDFATHER'S FULL NAME - 4

DATE OF BIRTH

PLACE OF BIRTH

DATE OF MARRIAGE

PLACE OF MARRIAGE

DATE OF DEATH

PLACE OF BURIAL

OCCUPATION

SPECIAL INTERESTS

GRANDMOTHER'S FULL NAME - 5

DATE OF BIRTH

PLACE OF BIRTH

DATE OF MARRIAGE

PLACE OF MARRIAGE

DATE OF DEATH

PLACE OF BURIAL

OCCUPATION

SPECIAL INTERESTS

MOTHER'S FULL NAME - 3

DATE OF BIRTH

PLACE OF BIRTH

DATE OF MARRIAGE

DATE OF DEATH

PLACE OF BURIAL

OCCUPATION

SPECIAL INTERESTS

Mother's Ancestry

GRANDFATHER'S FULL NAME - 6

DATE OF BIRTH

PLACE OF BIRTH

DATE OF MARRIAGE

PLACE OF MARRIAGE

DATE OF DEATH

PLACE OF BURIAL

OCCUPATION

SPECIAL INTERESTS

GRANDMOTHER'S FULL NAME - 7

DATE OF BIRTH

PLACE OF BIRTH

DATE OF MARRIAGE

PLACE OF MARRIAGE

DATE OF DEATH

PLACE OF BURIAL

OCCUPATION

SPECIAL INTERESTS

My Mother's Ancestral Chart

Father's Ancestry

GRANDFATHER'S FULL NAME - 6

DATE OF BIRTH   PLACE OF BIRTH

DATE OF MARRIAGE   PLACE OF MARRIAGE

DATE OF DEATH   PLACE OF BURIAL

OCCUPATION

SPECIAL INTERESTS

MOTHER'S FULL NAME - 3

DATE OF BIRTH   PLACE OF BIRTH

DATE OF MARRIAGE   PLACE OF MARRIAGE

DATE OF DEATH   PLACE OF BURIAL

MOTHER'S BROTHERS & SISTERS

GRANDMOTHER'S FULL NAME - 7

DATE OF BIRTH   PLACE OF BIRTH

DATE OF MARRIAGE

DATE OF DEATH   PLACE OF BURIAL

OCCUPATION

SPECIAL INTERESTS

Mother's Ancestry

GREAT GRANDFATHER'S FULL NAME - 12

DATE OF BIRTH   PLACE OF BIRTH

DATE OF MARRIAGE   PLACE OF MARRIAGE

DATE OF DEATH   PLACE OF BURIAL

OCCUPATION

SPECIAL INTERESTS

GREAT GRANDMOTHER'S FULL NAME - 13

DATE OF BIRTH   PLACE OF BIRTH

DATE OF MARRIAGE   PLACE OF MARRIAGE

DATE OF DEATH   PLACE OF BURIAL

OCCUPATION

SPECIAL INTERESTS

GREAT GRANDFATHER'S FULL NAME - 14

DATE OF BIRTH   PLACE OF BIRTH

DATE OF MARRIAGE   PLACE OF MARRIAGE

DATE OF DEATH   PLACE OF BURIAL

OCCUPATION

SPECIAL INTERESTS

GREAT GRANDMOTHER'S FULL NAME - 15

DATE OF BIRTH   PLACE OF BIRTH

DATE OF MARRIAGE   PLACE OF MARRIAGE

DATE OF DEATH   PLACE OF BURIAL

OCCUPATION

SPECIAL INTERESTS

My Family

My Brothers and Sisters and their Children:

Remarriages: Include the dates of divorce or death and the names of Spouses and Children.

Your immediate family was the center of your childhood and probably still plays an important role in your life. Because your brothers and sisters, if you had any, shared experiences with you, your recollections of them form part of your own history. Fill in your name, the date and place of your birth, along with those of your brothers and sisters. Then try to reconstruct the world in which you lived. Where did you reside? What did you and your brothers and sisters do as children? Do you remember any favorite games or memorable occasions, such as a party or a trip? Also record the history of your brothers' and sisters' adult lives: their education, occupation, places of residence, marriages, as well as the names and birthdates of their children—your nieces and nephews.

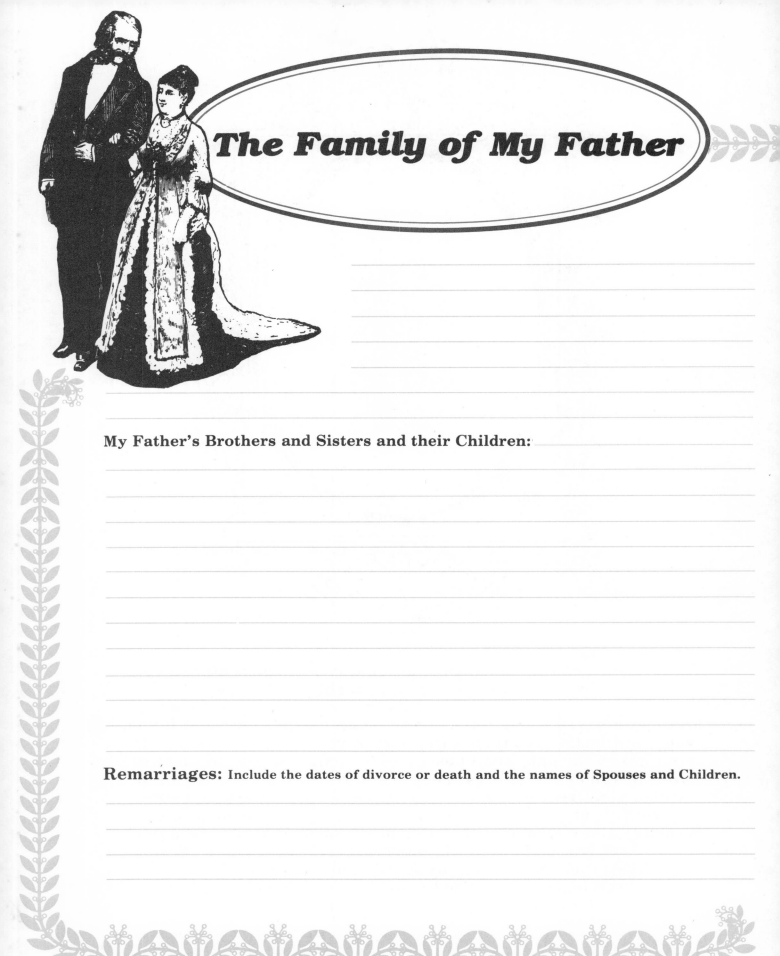

The Family of My Father

My Father's Brothers and Sisters and their Children:

Remarriages: Include the dates of divorce or death and the names of Spouses and Children.

*T*he world in which your parents grew up might have been very different from yours, but at the same time it determined the course of your life. When and where were your parents born? Where did they meet and when did they marry? What were their occupations? Parents often remind their children about how things have changed since their own youth. Perhaps your mother and father witnessed the invention of sound movies or the development of commercial aviation. Moreover, your parents once formed part of another family, some of whose members you may know yourself. So include the vital statistics of your parents' brothers and sisters (your aunts and uncles) as well as those of their children (your cousins).

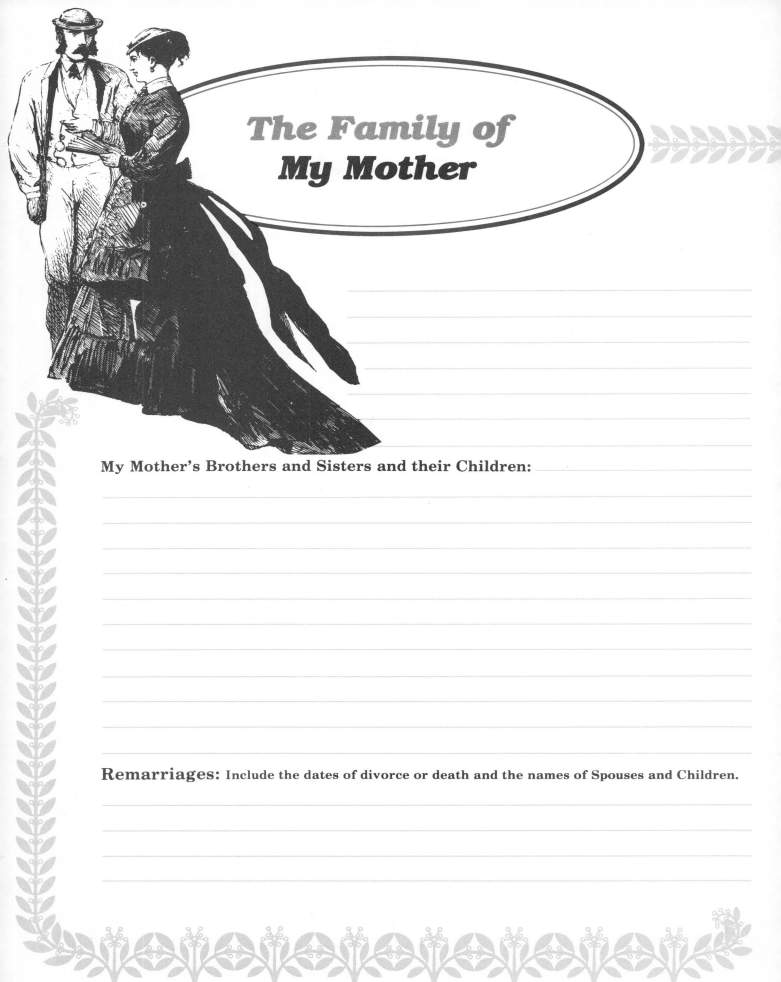

The Family of My Mother

_____

_____

_____

_____

_____

My Mother's Brothers and Sisters and their Children: _____

_____

_____

_____

_____

_____

_____

_____

_____

_____

Remarriages: Include the dates of divorce or death and the names of Spouses and Children.

_____

_____

_____

_____

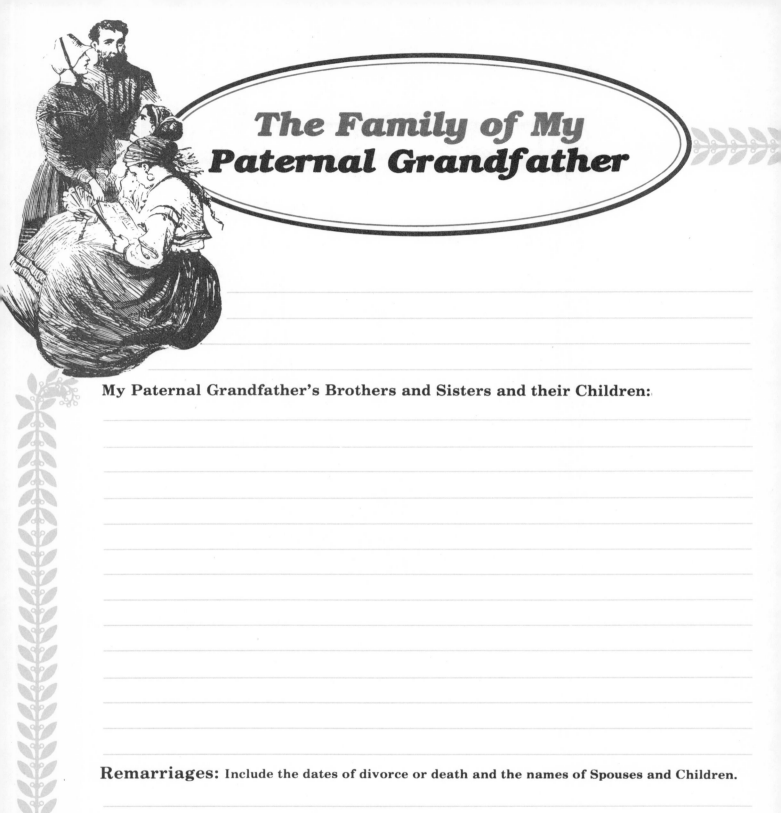

The Family of My Paternal Grandfather

_____

_____

_____

_____

My Paternal Grandfather's Brothers and Sisters and their Children:

_____

_____

_____

_____

_____

_____

_____

_____

_____

_____

_____

_____

_____

Remarriages: Include the dates of divorce or death and the names of Spouses and Children.

_____

_____

_____

_____

*T*he further you go back in time, the more difficult it becomes to find first-hand accounts of your ancestors. For most people, grandparents are the oldest generation with which they have personal contact. If you knew or still know your father's parents (your paternal grandparents,) did they reminisce with you about their youth, or did your father pass on any stories? After writing in your paternal grandparents' names and relevant dates, recount these anecdotes, particularly those that reveal characteristic habits, interests, or the kind of lives they led. And in order to keep a record of your paternal grandparents' own immediate families, note down the names and dates of their brothers and sisters (your great-aunts and great-uncles) and their children. Of course, any personal memories you may have of these people will make the account of your paternal grandparents all the more vivid.

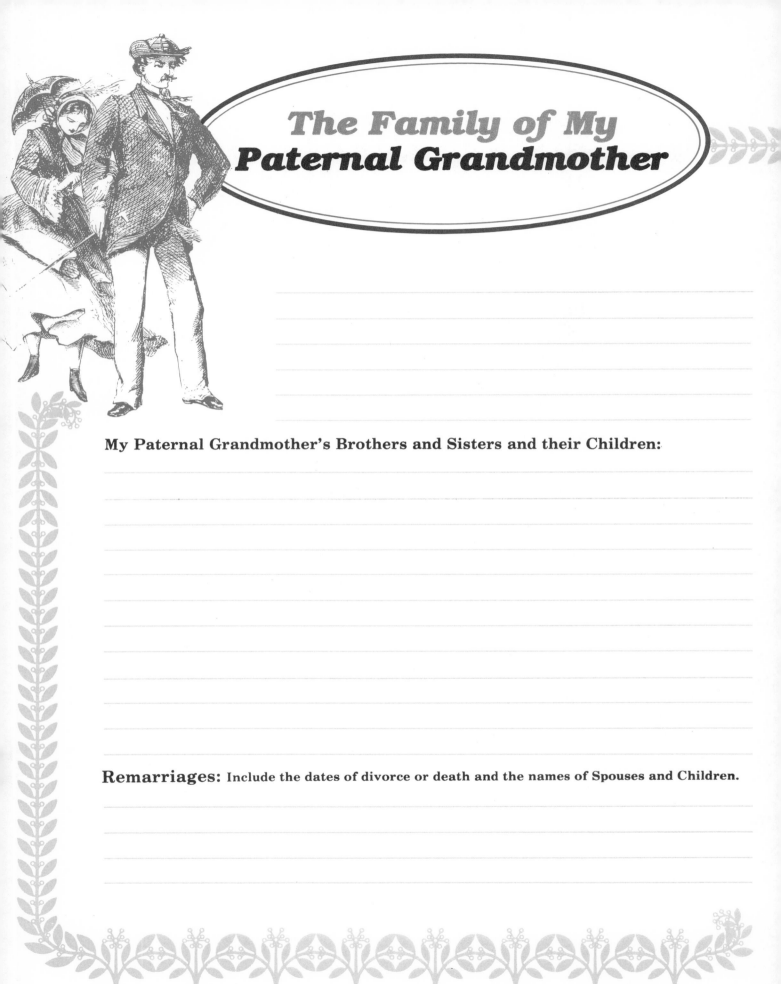

The Family of My
Paternal Grandmother

My Paternal Grandmother's Brothers and Sisters and their Children:

Remarriages: Include the dates of divorce or death and the names of Spouses and Children.

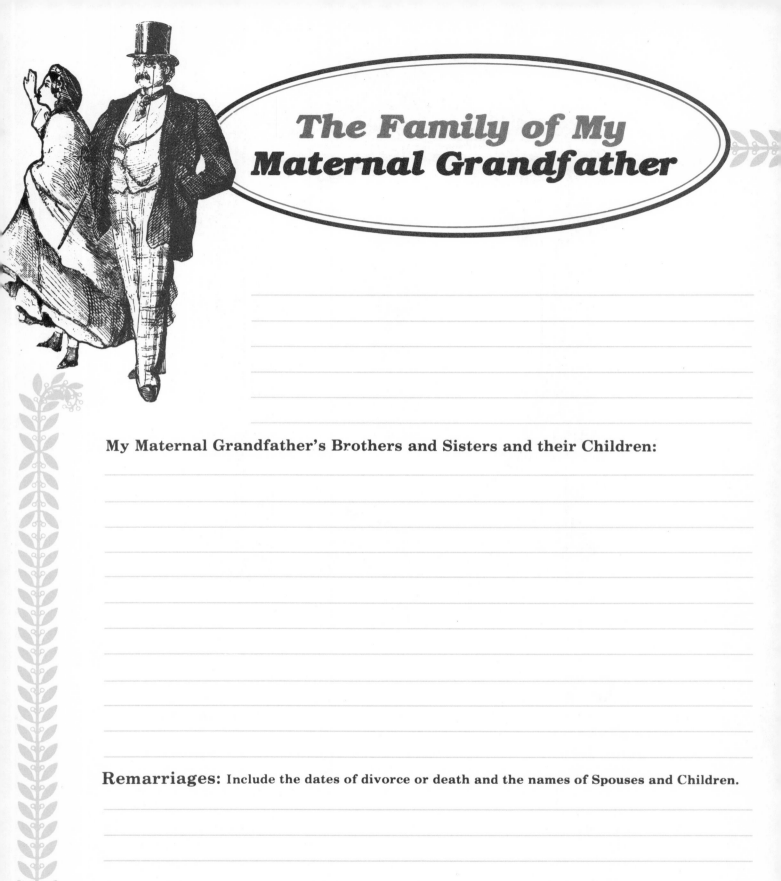

The Family of My Maternal Grandfather

_____

_____

_____

_____

_____

My Maternal Grandfather's Brothers and Sisters and their Children:

_____

_____

_____

_____

_____

_____

_____

_____

_____

_____

_____

Remarriages: Include the dates of divorce or death and the names of Spouses and Children.

_____

_____

_____

_____

You may also have known your mother's parents—your maternal grandparents. Record their vital statistics here, along with those of their brothers, sisters, and children. Like your paternal grandparents, your maternal grandparents can no doubt remember a childhood vastly different from your own. Your maternal grandmother may have grown up at a time when women's skirts always reached below the ankles, when bikinis were unheard of, and when landing men on the moon was strictly the stuff of science fiction. Into this historical picture, try to incorporate your own reminiscences of your grandparents and in this way illuminate their role in your family's life.

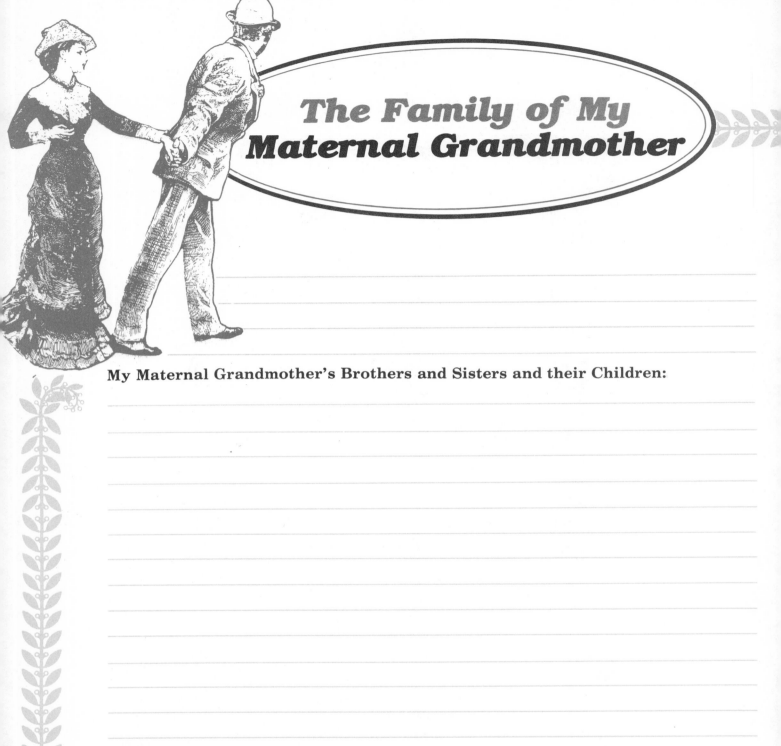

The Family of My Maternal Grandmother

My Maternal Grandmother's Brothers and Sisters and their Children:

Remarriages: Include the dates of divorce or death and the names of Spouses and Children.

The Families of My Great-Grandparents

My Paternal Great-Grandfather's Brothers and Sisters and their Children:

My Paternal Great-Grandmother's Brothers and Sisters and their Children:

Remarriages: Include the dates of divorce or death and the names of Spouses and Children.

List whatever names and dates you can find in family records or can learn from your parents and grandparents. Then try to imagine the environment in which your great-grandparents lived. If your grandparents grew up with different customs and witnessed events you now read about in history books, then your great-grandparents knew a world even more remote. They were probably born between a hundred and a hundred and fifty years ago—at a time when there were few large cities and the population was predominantly agricultural. Did your great-grandparents own or work on a farm? Are there any stories handed down about your great-grandparents that reveal their personalities, their accomplishments, or their relationship with other members of the family?

The Families of My Great-Grandparents

My Maternal Great-Grandfather's Brothers and Sisters and their Children:

My Maternal Great-Grandmother's Brothers and Sisters and their Children:

Remarriages: Include the dates of divorce or death and the names of Spouses and Children.

Family Weddings

Weddings are joyous events in every family. They not only provide an opportunity for the family to gather together and celebrate, but each wedding also opens a new chapter in the family history. The bride and groom, having left their immediate families, are about to start a family of their own—to add another branch to the genealogial tree. Keeping an account of these occasions is therefore a major contribution to your family's records. So try to expand the list of names and dates with recollections of the wedding party or reception, where the ceremony took place, and whether you participated in it.

Family Weddings

CONTINUED

Other Religious Ceremonies in My Family

Religious ceremonies usually mark off important milestones in children's lives. Whether baptism or circumcision, communion or bar mitzvah, these events are memorable stations on the road to adulthood. In the space below, fill in the names of the children (including yourself), the kind of ceremony held, where and when it took place, as well as the names of any godparents or sponsors and a brief description of how the occasion was celebrated.

My Family's Religious Affiliations

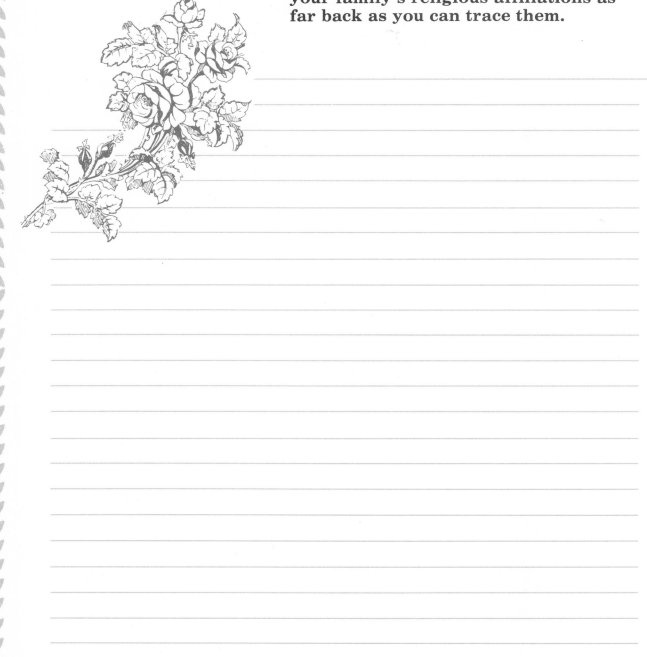

ecord here the religious history of your family. Were any relations clergymen? Did any belong to a religious order? Remember, too, that families, through marriage or conversion, change religions over the generations and may even now have members that practice different faiths. So be sure to include an account of your family's religious affiliations as far back as you can trace them.

Where I Have Worshipped

se this page to record your family's places of worship—the names of the congregations, their locations, the clergymen, and the period during which you and your family attended. Include also any information that describes your family's role in the church or synagogue. Did you or any other member, for example, participate in the activities or administration of the congregation?

Special Memories

A family history such as this is bound to include references to people who have died, and of whom you have no personal recollections. But at the same time there will be others whom you did know with whom you shared very special conversations and experiences. In order to preserve this information for yourself and provide future generations with a living picture of their ancestors, write down the names of these people and your memories of them.

Special Memories

CONTINUED

My Family's Homes

A record of your family's residences discloses a great deal about its history and activities. So add to the list of addresses and dates any facts that will enrich the account. Why did you or your family move? Was the new house or apartment larger or smaller? Was it in the city or in the country? Did the move affect you or others in a special way—for instance, causing a change in schools or jobs?

Street Address

City _____ State _____

Date of Purchase _____ Resided from _____ to _____

Street Address

City _____ State _____

Date of Purchase _____ Resided from _____ to _____

Street Address _____

City _____ **State** _____

Date of Purchase _____ **Resided from** _____ to _____

Street Address _____

City _____ **State** _____

Date of Purchase _____ **Resided from** _____ to _____

Street Address

City   **State**

Date of Purchase

Resided from   **to**

Street Address

City   **State**

Date of Purchase

Resided from   **to**

Street Address

City   **State**

Date of Purchase   **Resided from**   **to**

My Family's Homes

CONTINUED

Street Address

City   **State**

Date of Purchase   **Resided from**   **to**

Street Address

City   **State**

Date of Purchase

Resided from   **to**

Street Address

City   **State**

Date of Purchase

Resided from   **to**

The Schools I Have Attended

*I*nclude here your educational backgrounds and those of the family. Such an account is not only an individual record, but also a good measure of your family's accomplishments. Following the list of schools and degrees, write down any outstanding achievements, scholastic activities, or interests— participation in sports, awards, grades, and so forth. Use the remaining space for personal reminiscences of favorite teachers, classmates, subjects studied, or graduation gifts and celebrations.

	Name	School	Date Graduated	Degree
1				
2				
3				
4				
5				
6				
7				
8				
9				
10				
11				

	Name	School	Date Graduated	Degree
1				
2				
3				
4				
5				
6				
7				
8				
9				
10				
11				

The Schools I Have Attended

CONTINUED

The Organizations I Have Joined

People have always sought out others with whom to share interests or work for a common cause. In the last hundred or so years, as people acquired more and more leisure time, they not only organized professionally, but also formed clubs to pursue their hobbies, publicize their political views, or collect charity. By writing down the names of the organizations to which you and other family members belonged, along with recollections of the person or the group, you can retell the story of your family's role in the life of the community.

Professions, Occupations, Crafts & Trades

Where the members of your family resided, what schools they attended, and the quality of their lives were probably determined by the jobs they held. So use the space below to enter the employment record of your family. Also give an account of any family businesses that were started— where, when, by whom, and the reasons for success or failure. At the end of the the section, don't forget to add the employment registration numbers (social security numbers, for instance) assigned to each person by the government. Since many government bureaus file documents according to such numbers, the list will be invaluable for others.

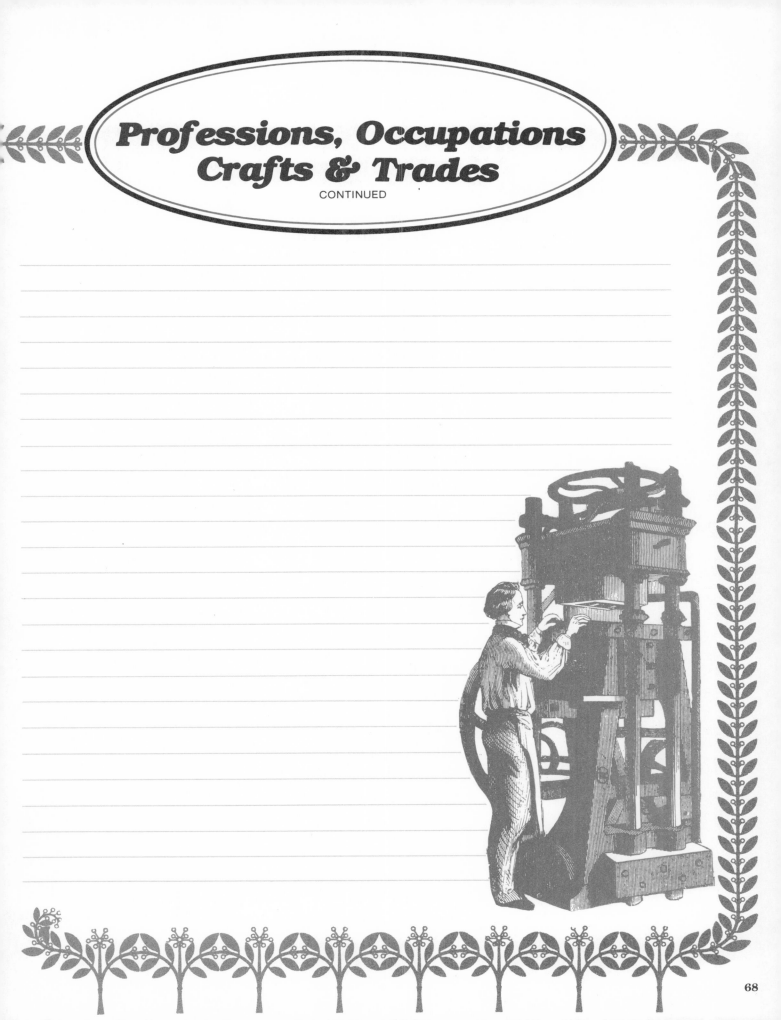

My Family's Military Service Record

An individual's military service is more than a personal event. A prolonged absence, an injury, or even death often mark a crucial moment in the history of the whole family. Although the information to be filled in below seems detailed and complex, it may not be difficult to obtain. Probably no branch of the government creates and maintains such an abundance of records and documents as does the armed forces. And in the case of an ancestor who did military service for a foreign country and whose records may therefore have been lost or destroyed, try to write down whatever can be learned from other members of the family.

NAME   SERVICE NUMBER   RANK

INDUCTED   MONTH   DAY   YEAR   AT AGE

BRANCH OF SERVICE   GRADE

DIVISION   REGIMENT   DEPARTMENT OR SHIP

REMARKS

NAME   SERVICE NUMBER   RANK

INDUCTED   MONTH   DAY   YEAR   AT AGE

BRANCH OF SERVICE   GRADE

DIVISION   REGIMENT   DEPARTMENT OR SHIP   DATES

REMARKS

NAME   SERVICE NUMBER   RANK

INDUCTED   MONTH   DAY   YEAR   AT AGE

BRANCH OF SERVICE   GRADE

DIVISION   REGIMENT   DEPARTMENT OR SHIP   DATES

REMARKS

NAME   SERVICE NUMBER   RANK

INDUCTED   MONTH   DAY   YEAR   AT AGE

BRANCH OF SERVICE   GRADE

DIVISION   REGIMENT   DEPARTMENT OR SHIP   DATES

REMARKS   TRANSFERRED

NAME _____ SERVICE NUMBER _____ RANK _____

INDUCTED _____ MONTH _____ DAY _____ YEAR _____ AT AGE _____

BRANCH OF SERVICE _____ GRADE _____

DIVISION _____ REGIMENT _____ DEPARTMENT OR SHIP _____ DATES _____

REMARKS _____ TRANSFERRED _____

_____

_____

_____

_____

_____

_____

_____

NAME _____ SERVICE NUMBER _____ RANK _____

INDUCTED _____ MONTH _____ DAY _____ YEAR _____ AT AGE _____

BRANCH OF SERVICE _____ GRADE _____

DIVISION _____ REGIMENT _____ DEPARTMENT OR SHIP _____ DATES _____

REMARKS _____

_____

_____

_____

_____

_____

_____

_____

_____

_____

My Family's Military Service Record

CONTINUED

NAME _____ SERVICE NUMBER _____ RANK _____

INDUCTED _____ MONTH _____ DAY _____ YEAR _____ AT AGE _____

BRANCH OF SERVICE _____ GRADE _____

DIVISION _____ REGIMENT _____ DEPARTMENT OR SHIP _____ DATES _____

REMARKS _____ TRANSFERRED _____

_____

_____

_____

_____

_____

_____

NAME _____ SERVICE NUMBER _____ RANK _____

INDUCTED _____ MONTH _____ DAY _____ YEAR _____ AT AGE _____

BRANCH OF SERVICE _____ GRADE _____

DIVISION _____ REGIMENT _____ DEPARTMENT OR SHIP _____

REMARKS _____ DATES _____

_____

_____

_____

_____

_____

_____

_____

My Best Friends

A family register should also include close friends who, although not blood relations, are usually a part of the family life. Since a good friend is like a brother or sister—someone in whom we confide and with whom we share experiences—this book would be incomplete without a record of each one. So write down their names, addresses, when you knew them, and what it was that made the friends so special. Remember, too, that friends may be able to provide vital information about family members for you or future generations.

The Pets in My Family

For a child growing up, or even for an adult, a pet is like a special friend—a member of the family. Whether a cat, dog, horse, fish, turtle, monkey, or some more exotic creature, animals claim a daily part of a family's attention. In addition to recording vital statistics, therefore, try to create a portrait of each pet with a description of how it was acquired, its temperament, best tricks, favorite foods, and how you or the family cared for it.

The Automobile

My Mechanical Companion

Nothing has changed the character of modern living as radically as the automobile. Not only can we do errands, get to work or to school more quickly, but we can also travel long distances to visit friends and relations. In this way, the automobile plays an important role in almost every family's life. Moreover, each car owned by you or your family may help to recall special events or circumstances in the family story.

Special Things

Your favorite things reveal a great deal about your own personality. Favorite things may be sports, vacation spots, songs, recipes, and games. Or they may be objects like books, records, toys, and paintings. In each case, a listing of these things forms a kind of brief character study, a written portrait of yourself.

Special Things

(CONTINUED)

My Prized Family Possessions

The objects passed down from generation to generation are as much a part of the family record as are names, dates, and events. Whether furniture, jewelry, art, a library, or a stamp collection, such things help make the past visible to the present. To read a book owned by your parents, or wear a necklace worn by your great-grandmother, or sit in the same chair in which your grandfather sat, is to become a living participant in your family's ongoing history. Try, therefore, to inventory the heirlooms, noting their original owners and how they came into your possession. Do the same for any collections formed by your ancestors that are still intact. And don't forget to include precious objects newly purchased or collections now being started, for these will be the heirlooms of tomorrow.

Prized Family Possessions

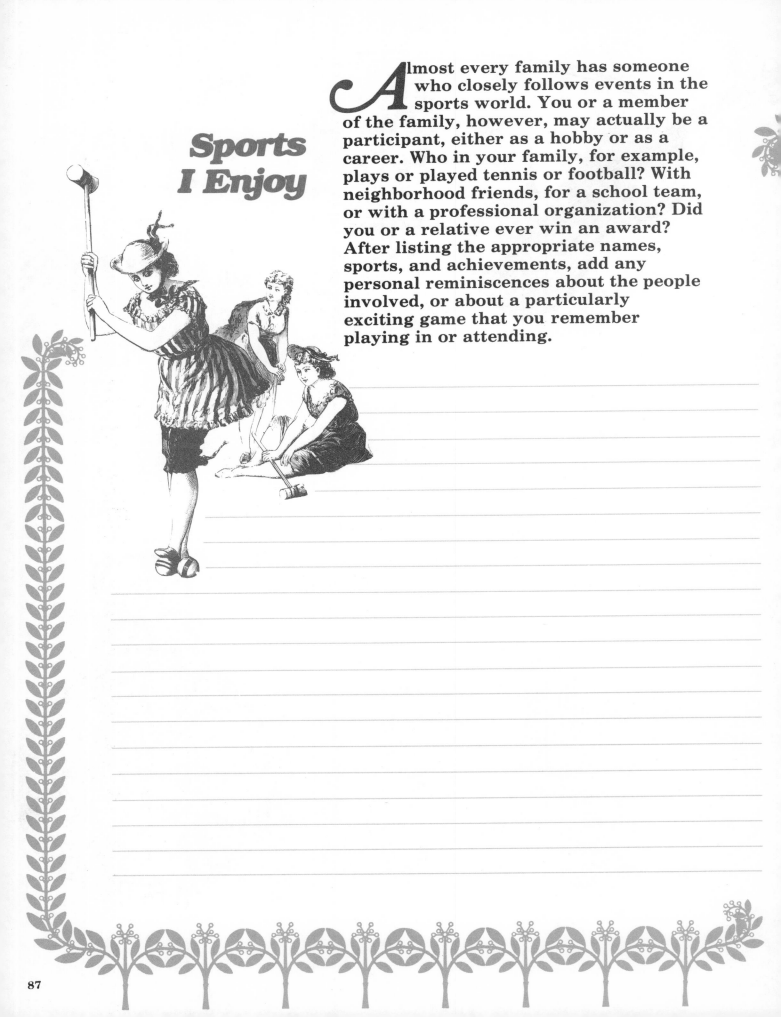

Sports I Enjoy

Almost every family has someone who closely follows events in the sports world. You or a member of the family, however, may actually be a participant, either as a hobby or as a career. Who in your family, for example, plays or played tennis or football? With neighborhood friends, for a school team, or with a professional organization? Did you or a relative ever win an award? After listing the appropriate names, sports, and achievements, add any personal reminiscences about the people involved, or about a particularly exciting game that you remember playing in or attending.

Sports I Enjoy

CONTINUED

My Family's Hobbies

What people do in their spare time, no matter how common or unusual, is often the most fascinating part of their personal histories. Have you a relative who makes pottery, breeds dogs, takes photographs, flies kites, does carpentry, collects butterflies, or sews? What hobbies do you pursue? Use this space to record the names and pastimes, how each person began, and what they accomplished. Are there any hobbies in which the entire family participates? Perhaps, too, you can recall a prize-winning achievement or have some treasured object that a relative made.

My Family's Hobbies

CONTINUED

Memorable Vacations

For most of us, vacations are a wonderful break from everyday routine. We can relax and get away from it all without the pressures of school, work, or domestic responsibilities. Do you go on holidays by yourself or does the whole family take off for the seashore, the ski slopes, or a cross-country journey? Some vacations no doubt made for memorable occasions. Describe them below—where you went, when, with whom—so that the family can relive these vacations and you can keep a precious record for later years.

Memorable Vacations

(CONTINUED)

Family Gatherings

*S*ince many families do not reside in the same town, the family reunion is a joyful opportunity to see loved ones and renew cherished relationships. The reunions you describe here may have taken place by tradition at a particular time of the year, or the family may just have gotten together to celebrate holidays, special birthdays, or anniversaries. And whatever the occasion, use future meetings to gather information about the family's history. Don't forget to enter those reunions attended by you.

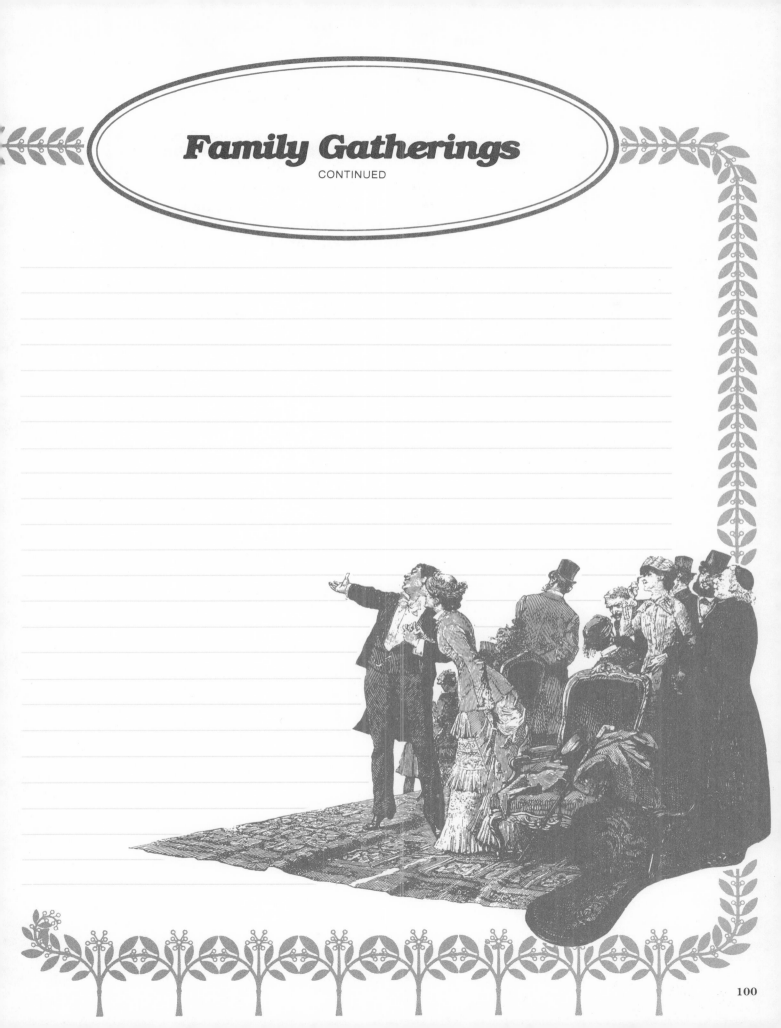

Cherished Traditions

Reunions are of course part of a family's traditions. But there are also customs in each family that live on, even when the members are separated, and help to give the family its own special character. It may be a special style of cooking handed down through the generations, or a unique way of commemorating birthdays. Perhaps members of your family always attend the same schools or take up similar professions. Is there a favorite repertory of stories invariably told to each generation of children? Whatever the traditions, enrich the picture of your family's heritage by entering them on these pages.

The Most Outstanding Events In My Family's History

There may be unusual events or proud achievements in your family that cannot be easily categorized. Was anyone in the family, for instance, ever honored for outstanding service to their country or city? Did anyone make a technological invention or advance scientific knowledge? Perhaps you or a family member knew or met a famous personality, witnessed a history-making speech, or published a book. Use the space below to record these things.

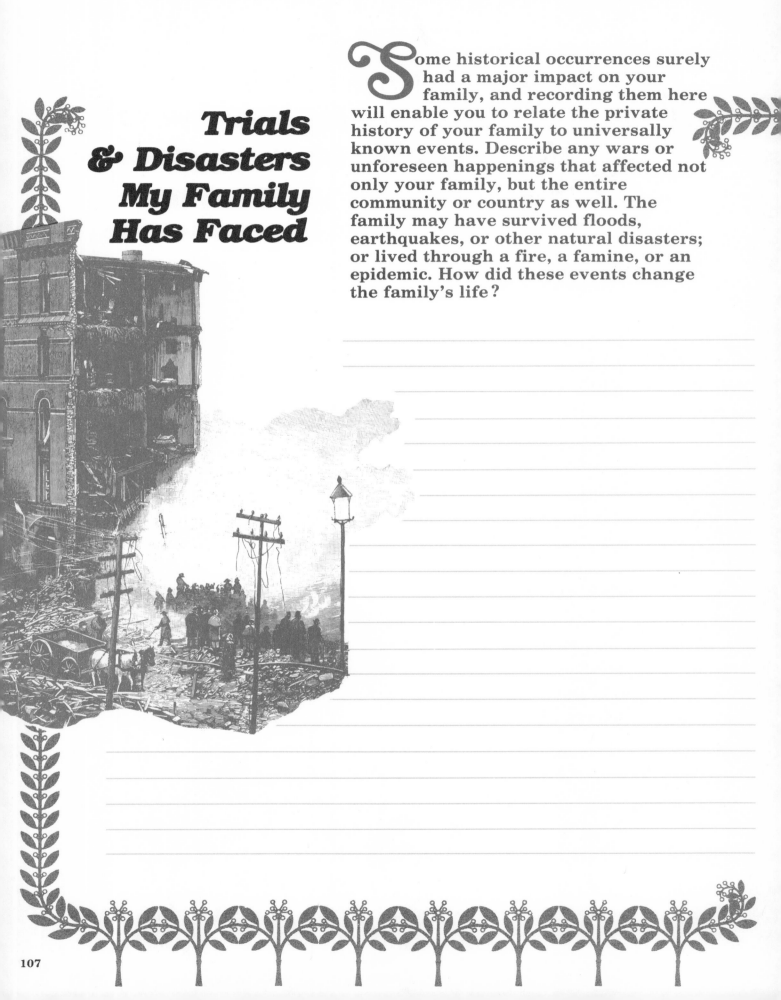

Trials & Disasters My Family Has Faced

Some historical occurrences surely had a major impact on your family, and recording them here will enable you to relate the private history of your family to universally known events. Describe any wars or unforeseen happenings that affected not only your family, but the entire community or country as well. The family may have survived floods, earthquakes, or other natural disasters; or lived through a fire, a famine, or an epidemic. How did these events change the family's life?

The Oral History of My Family

Every family has stories that have been told from generation to generation. Such tales may involve heroic deeds, great achievements, fortunate escapes from disaster or political repression. Or they may recount personal anecdotes about how people met and married, where they traveled, and whom they knew. In all likelihood, these stories have never been written down. By doing so here you can preserve them for the future.

The Oral History of My Family
CONTINUED

My Family's Medical History

*I*llnesses are a sad but unavoidable feature of life. List here the names of those who were sick. Because some illnesses are hereditary, you may be recording vital information for future generations. In the remaining space, add your personal recollections and, if necessary, an account of how each illness altered the family's life.

Vital Statistics

As we grow older, many things about us change. In this section you can record your present physical traits, clothes sizes, color preferences, and so on. The statistics will provide a handy guide for today, as well as give future generations a better idea of you. Along with the pictures in the photo section, you can look back, years from now, and see exactly what you and the family were like in 19 ____ .

ME

Age _____ Height _____

Weight _____

Hair Color _____

Color of Eyes _____

Suit Size _____

Shirt Size _____

Waist _____

Shoe Size _____

Hat Size _____

Ring Size _____

Other Sizes _____

_____

_____

Color Preference _____

_____

_____

Perfume & Toiletries Preference _____

_____

_____

MOTHER

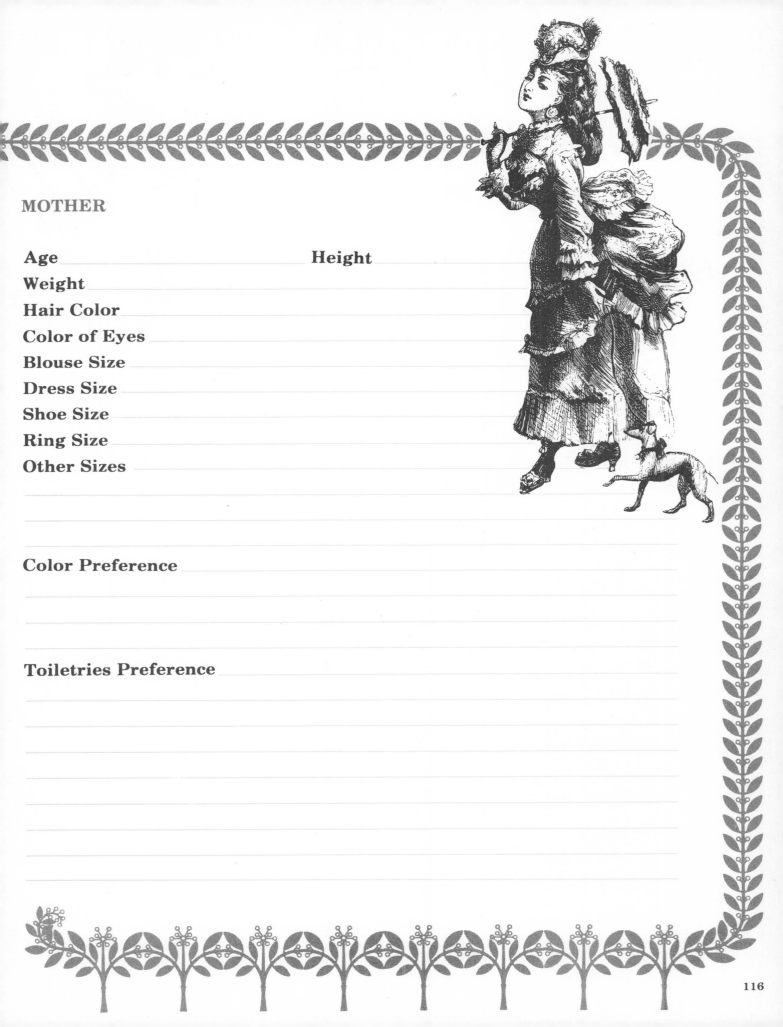

Age _____ Height _____

Weight _____

Hair Color _____

Color of Eyes _____

Blouse Size _____

Dress Size _____

Shoe Size _____

Ring Size _____

Other Sizes _____

_____

Color Preference _____

_____

_____

Toiletries Preference _____

_____

_____

_____

_____

_____

_____

FATHER

Age _____	Height _____
Weight _____	
Hair Color _____	
Color of Eyes _____	
Suit Size _____	
Shirt Size _____	
Shoe Size _____	
Hat Size _____	
Ring Size _____	
Other Sizes _____	

Color Preference

Perfume & Toiletries Preference

Vital Statistics

CONTINUED

BROTHERS—SISTERS—FRIENDS

Name	Age	Height	Weight	Suit, Dress Size	Blouse, Shirt Size	Other Sizes

Photographs

Pictures do their own story telling and in years to come a lot can be learned from this kind of record. You and future generations will be able to look back and see a member of the family in his or her own time and place. (You may also want to include favorite clippings, mementos, or documents.)

Photographs

CONTINUED

Photographs

CONTINUED

Genealogy Research

Genealogy research can be an enjoyable and rewarding experience if you approach it with curiosity and determination. Remember that you are carrying out this search to illuminate your own special history, so whatever you find will disclose a good deal about your heritage. Above all, don't get discouraged. Tracing ancestors can take you so far into the past and to such distant places that the task may sometimes seem hopeless. But, as experienced genealogists know, perseverance will win out. Moreover, your pursuit of history will open up worlds of new people, new places, and friendly organizations.

The procedure outlined here will start you on the right road. Where that road leads, how it branches off, will be determined by the unique make-up of your ancestral group. Because no one's heritage is like anyone else's, the possibilities are almost infinite. So after following the general suggestions, begin your own detective work, tracking down each clue as it comes in, writing to those agencies and using those reference books that are relevant to your particular quest. Once again, the task is less formidable than it seems. Genealogy is frequently a well-marked, step-by-step process, with one set of facts clearly pointing the way to the next. Each ancestor or each generation is bound to have some identifying feature—an occupation or a residence, for example—that will tell you where to turn for information. It is as if your forebears were stretching their hands across time to guide you in your search.

Begin this search with the people around you. Interviewing relatives and family friends can uncover a wealth of names and statistics. Ask the family for the full names and dates of all the members they can recall. Don't be surprised if you suddenly learn of relatives you didn't know existed. People often forget about those who died a long time ago or who lived in another country and your questions will stimulate reluctant memories. Also ask relatives for any personal recollections about your ancestors. This is the only way to bring together the oral tradition of the family, which you now can preserve in written form.

Then start hunting—and encourage others to hunt—in attics, basements, and storerooms for family records. These records may take the form of documents, old letters, Bibles, photo albums, portraits, diaries, or even engraved jewelry and other heirlooms. Whatever you discover will no doubt supply additional names and dates, as well as a picture of the individuals. Even your grandmother's wedding dress or your grandfather's service medals are useful finds, for they reveal the kind of world in which these people lived and what they accomplished.

The telephone directory often turns out to be the genealogist's best reference tool. Local libraries usually keep old directories. Look for your surname in the ones that cover the period during which your family lived in the town. You may already know some of the names and the telephone book will tell you exactly where each person resided and, if you check from year to year, for how long. Don't forget to consider spelling changes in the family name. In addition, study the listings for your surname in a current directory. Are there any people with whom you are not acquainted? If so, send them the names and dates of your parents and grandparents and ask if they might be related. (Of course, if your surname is too common, this is not a practical step.) When you do come upon new relations in this way, ask them to try and fill in the missing pieces.

For the genealogist, even stones speak—tombstones, that is. Once you find out where an ancestor died, pay a visit to the local cemetery. A gravestone inscription will furnish the precise years of birth and death and sometimes even the months and days—statistics that are invaluable for future research. And the epitaph may disclose the name of a spouse, describe how the family felt about the deceased, or cite some impressive accomplishment. If no gravestone can be found, stop by at the cemetery office and check the records—not only for your known ancestors, but for those who bore the same name.

The next step is to pore over the records of the town in which you live or where your relations resided. All governments preserve records and local administrations are no exception. Armed with the ancestor's names and, if possible, significant dates, you may be able to reconstruct large parts of their lives with the information obtained from certificates of birth, marriage, divorce, or death; or from probated wills, tax and property assessments, and business incorporations or sales.

Schools are also inveterate record-keepers. Every public school, college, and university keeps a detailed account of its students. If you know where and approximately when someone was educated, ask the school authorities to check through the files for your relative's name. They just might hand you a marvelously complete report of grades, activities, and achievements!

Religious foundations, too, can be important sources of material. Most churches and synagogues maintain records of their congregations, or at least of the ceremonies that took place within their walls. And a certificate of baptism or confirmation, a copy of a wedding license or an entry for a funeral will supply essential names and dates. If you do not know to which congregation an ancestor belonged, visit or write to all the places of worship in the neighborhood where he or she resided.

The public library of every town or city is a storehouse of genealogical data. Not only does it house a good stock of reference books on the subject of genealogy research, but it probably has bound lists of births, marriages, and deaths, as well as copies of deeds and other civic documents—often dating back a century or more. Libraries also furnish old newspapers, usually preserved on microfilm. Take the date on which someone died and read the appropriate obituary columns for a mention of age, survivors, achievements, and the location of the funeral service.

Many towns, cities, states, counties, or provinces have local historical or genealogical associations that will be happy to offer assistance. Through them, moreover, you can meet other researchers with whom to exchange stories and share helpful hints.

Now you must move on to the national archives of your country— the repositories for all the vital statistics collected by census bureaus, immigration departments, and the armed forces. Census reports give you the age, occupation, place of birth, and exact residence of a relative during a particular year, in addition to the number and identity of the other family members living under the same roof. Immigration records contain the name of the ship on which someone traveled, when it arrived, its port of entry, and the date of the immigrant's naturalization. A relative who worked for the government will also have a civil service record filed in the national archives. And remember that much of the information you seek can be solicited by letter.

It is at this point that each person's path of research branches out into innumerably diverse trails. The names and addresses of the national archives for the major English-speaking countries of the world appear at the end of this section. If they do not have the required data, they may advise you where to turn; or you may consult the reference books available in your library. By this time you will have accumulated enough details about your family's history to be able to exclude some avenues of research and focus sharply on others.

If you want to trace ancestors back to a foreign country, there are three basic lines of pursuit. First, many of the books in your library provide nation-by-nation lists of the names and addresses of people and agencies throughout the world who assist genealogists in hunting down foreign-born relatives. Second, write to the consulate of the country from which your family came—the address will be in the telephone directory or can be obtained from your own government. Consulates frequently put you in touch with the proper agency in their native lands. When requesting information from a foreign organization, be as specific as possible and try to cite all the spelling variations and name changes you have come across. Don't hesitate to write in English—your correspondent will find a translator.

Lastly, there is the Genealogical Society of the Church of Jesus Christ of Latter-day Saints (50 East North Temple Street, Salt Lake City, Utah 84150.) For the last eighty years, this remarkable group has been amassing an enormous collection of genealogical records from towns, cities, churches, and private groups all around the world. To date, they have almost a million 100-foot rolls of microfilm stored in deep mountain vaults, and the collection is increasing at the rate of 50,000 reels a year. Over seven million family groups and thirty million individuals are indexed in their archives. So no matter where you presently live or what country your ancestors came from, a letter to the Genealogical Society is an important step in your research.

Good luck!

National Archives

UNITED STATES
National Archives and Records Service
General Services Administration
Washington, D.C. 20408

CANADA
Public Archives of Canada
395 rue Wellington
Ottawa, Ontario K1A ON3

ENGLAND
Public Record Office
Chancery Lane
London WC2A 1LR, England

IRELAND
National Archives
Kildare Street
Dublin 2, Ireland

NORTHERN IRELAND
The Public Record Office
66 Balmoral Avenue
Belfast BJ9 6NY, Northern Ireland

SCOTLAND
Scottish Record Office
P.O. Box 36
H.M. General Register House
Edinburgh EH1 3YT, Scotland

WALES
National Library of Wales
Aberystwyth, Dyfed
S423 3BU, Wales

AUSTRALIA
National Archives
71 Leichhardt St., Kingston
Australian Capital Territory
2604 Australia

NEW ZEALAND
National Archives
Borthswick House
85 The Terrace
Wellington 1, New Zealand

SOUTH AFRICA
Central Archives Depot
Union Buildings
Private Bag X236
Pretoria, Rep. of South Africa, 0001

RHODESIA
National Archives of Rhodesia
Gun Hill, Borrowdale Road
Private Bag 7729
Causeway, Salisbury, Rhodesia

Name _____ **Relationship** _____

Street Address _____

City _____ **State** _____

Zip _____ **Telephone: Area (   )** _____

Birth or Memorial Date _____ **Astrological Sign** _____

Name _____ **Relationship** _____

Street Address _____

City _____ **State** _____

Zip _____ **Telephone: Area (   )** _____

Birth or Memorial Date _____ **Astrological Sign** _____

Name _____ **Relationship** _____

Street Address _____

City _____ **State** _____

Zip _____ **Telephone: Area (   )** _____

Birth or Memorial Date _____ **Astrological Sign** _____

Name _____ **Relationship** _____

Street Address _____

City _____ **State** _____

Zip _____ **Telephone: Area (   )** _____

Birth or Memorial Date _____ **Astrological Sign** _____

Addresses

Name _____ Relationship _____
Street Address _____
City _____ State _____
Zip _____ Telephone: Area ( ) _____
Birth or Memorial Date _____ Astrological Sign _____

Name _____ Relationship _____
Street Address _____
City _____ State _____
Zip _____ Telephone: Area ( ) _____
Birth or Memorial Date _____ Astrological Sign _____

Name _____ Relationship _____
Street Address _____
City _____ State _____
Zip _____ Telephone: Area ( ) _____
Birth or Memorial Date _____ Astrological Sign _____

Name _____ Relationship _____
Street Address _____
City _____ State _____
Zip _____ Telephone: Area ( ) _____
Birth or Memorial Date _____ Astrological Sign _____

Name _____ **Relationship** _____

Street Address _____

City _____ **State** _____

Zip _____ **Telephone: Area (   )** _____

Birth or Memorial Date _____ **Astrological Sign** _____

Name _____ **Relationship** _____

Street Address _____

City _____ **State** _____

Zip _____ **Telephone: Area (   )** _____

Birth or Memorial Date _____ **Astrological Sign** _____

Name _____ **Relationship** _____

Street Address _____

City _____ **State** _____

Zip _____ **Telephone: Area (   )** _____

Birth or Memorial Date _____ **Astrological Sign** _____

Name _____ **Relationship** _____

Street Address _____

City _____ **State** _____

Zip _____ **Telephone: Area (   )** _____

Birth or Memorial Date _____ **Astrological Sign** _____

Addresses

Name _____ Relationship _____

Street Address _____

City _____ State _____

Zip _____ Telephone: Area (   ) _____

Birth or Memorial Date _____ Astrological Sign _____

Name _____ Relationship _____

Street Address _____

City _____ State _____

Zip _____ Telephone: Area (   ) _____

Birth or Memorial Date _____ Astrological Sign _____

Name _____ Relationship _____

Street Address _____

City _____ State _____

Zip _____ Telephone: Area (   ) _____

Birth or Memorial Date _____ Astrological Sign _____

Name _____ Relationship _____

Street Address _____

City _____ State _____

Zip _____ Telephone: Area (   ) _____

Birth or Memorial Date _____ Astrological Sign _____

Autographs

Autographs

(CONTINUED)